COME IN, ROSALYN! I'M SORRY! WE DIDN'T REALIZE CALVIN HADN'T LET YOU IN.

THAT'S OK. IT WASN'T *TOO* COLD AND WET OUT.

WE'RE LATE. HELP YOURSELF TO ANYTHING IN THE FRIDGE. WE'LL SEE YOU AT TEN.

THE DOOR WAS JAMMED. REALLY. I COULDN'T GET IT OPEN.

BED.

HEY, DON'T FIX *THAT* FOR DINNER! DIDN'T MOM TELL YOU HOBBES AND I ARE ON A STRICT BIG MAC DIET? IT'S DOCTOR'S ORDERS!

OH, I'D BETTER CALL YOUR DOCTOR THEN!

OH, NO, SHE CALLED MY BLUFF! THE DOCTOR'S GONNA BE FURIOUS! BOY, ARE WE GOING TO GET IT!

"WE"?

I'M DIALING!

HELLO, DOCTOR? I'M CALLING ABOUT CALVIN'S DIETARY NEEDS.

..AT THE TONE, THE TIME WILL BE 6:27 AND 10 SECONDS. *BEEP*

BAD NEWS, CALVIN. YOUR DOCTOR SAYS YOU SHOULD A SPOONFUL OF CASTOR OIL AND LIE DOWN ALL EVENIN

HE DID REALLY NO, HE DID DID HE WHAT'S CA OIL?

MOM DOESN'T SET THE TABLE THIS WAY. MOM DOES IT A LOT BETTER.

THIS FOOD SMELLS FUNNY. THIS ISN'T THE WAY MOM FIXES IT. I LIKE IT THE WAY MOM DOES IT BETTER.

I'M NOT YOUR MOM, ALL RIGHT?!

NO KIDDING! MY MOM LOV ME MORE THAN LIFE ITSE AND SHE LETS ME DO ANYTH I WANT. NOT LIKE *YOU*, YOU NASTY OL' BARRACUDA.

I CAN'T BEL I POSTPON A DATE FO THIS.

WEIRDOS FROM ANOTHER PLANET!

A Calvin and Hobbes Collection by Bill Watterson

SCHOLASTIC INC.
New York Toronto London Auckland Sydney

Calvin and Hobbes is syndicated internationally
by Universal Press Syndicate.

ISBN 0-590-44164-7

12 11 10 9 8 7 6 5 4 3 2   8 9/9

Printed in the U.S.A.   34

First Scholastic printing, September 1990

Hey, Calvin, guess what we're doing in gym today. We're wrestling!

Next period you'll be so covered with mat burns you'll need skin grafts! Ha ha ha! See ya then, twinky.

SIGHHHH...

PHYSICAL EDUCATION IS WHAT YOU LEARN FROM HAVING YOUR FACE IN SOMEONE'S ARMPIT RIGHT BEFORE LUNCH.

KAPWIINGGG! IT'S CALVIN, THE HUMAN LIGHT PARTICLE!

IN THE BLINK OF AN EYE, HE'S 165,000 MILES AWAY!

NOTHING IN THE UNIVERSE IS FASTER THAN CALVIN!

...I HOPE!

MUCH AS I LOVE MY "CHOCOLATE FROSTED CRUNCHY SUGAR BOMBS," THE BEST PART IS AFTER THE CEREAL IS GONE.

THAT'S WHEN YOU EAT THE LEFTOVER MILK THAT'S ALL SLUDGY FROM THE EXTRA SUGAR YOU ADDED.

SOMETIMES I EAT TWO OR THREE BOWLS OF THIS.

I CAN HEAR YOUR HEART RACING FROM HERE.

THEY MAKE THIS CEREAL WITH MARSHMALLOW BITS, TOO, BUT MOM WON'T BUY IT FOR ME.

CALVIN and HOBBES

by WATERSON

IT'S FREEZING UPSTAIRS!

CAN I TAKE SOME LOGS UP TO MY ROOM?

HEY, YOU'RE ON MY SIDE OF THE BED.

THESE SHEETS ARE FREEZING!

YEAH, WELL... AAUGHH! YOUR FEET ARE LIKE ICE! GET AWAY FROM ME!

BUT MY SIDE'S ALL COLD!

WELL DON'T GET *ME* COLD! MOVE OVER!

SURE, *YOU'VE* GOT A FUR COAT! I'M JUST WEARING PAJAMAS.

QUIT PULLING THE BLANKETS, WILLYA?

I HARDLY HAVE ANY, YOU HOG! GIMME THOSE!

YOU'RE LETTING IN COLD AIR! QUIT IT! QUIT IT!

SERVES YOU RIGHT, MR. MOSTY-TOASTY! SEE WHAT IT'S LIKE BEING COLD!

YAAAAH!!

EAT FEATHERS, FUZZ BALL!

WHAP OOF ZROW

MOVE OVER. YOU'RE GETTING MY SIDE ALL HOT.

OPEN THE WINDOW. I'M ROASTING.

WHAT'S YOUR TAIL FOR?

MY TAIL?

YEAH. WHY DO TIGERS NEED TAILS?

GEE, I'M NOT REALLY SURE.

I GUESS JUST BECAUSE THEY LOOK GOOD.

SO IT'S SORT OF A NECKTIE FOR YOUR BUTT?

LET'S NOT BE VULGAR. YOU'RE JUST JEALOUS.

I THINK RITUALS ARE IMPORTANT.

MY FAVORITE RITUAL IS EATING THREE BOWLS OF "CHOCOLATE FROSTED SUGAR BOMBS" AND WATCHING TV CARTOONS ALL SATURDAY MORNING.

AFTER A FEW HOURS, I'M SO OVERSTIMULATED I CAN'T SIT STILL OR EVEN THINK STRAIGHT.

SORT OF A TRANSCENDENTAL EXPERIENCE, HUH?

YEAH. I ACHIEVE A LOWER CONSCIOUSNESS.

HOBBES, YOU'RE SUPPOSED TO BE TEACHING ME HOW TO BE A TIGER.

WE'VE BEEN SITTING IN THIS DUMB TREE ALL MORNING, AND YOU HAVEN'T TAUGHT ME HOW TO HUNT OR ANYTHING!

IT'S INSTINCT. YOU CAN'T TEACH THAT.

WELL IF YOU WON'T HELP, I'LL JUST GO LOOK UP "TIGER" IN THE ENCYCLOPEDIA.

AS LONG AS WE'RE GOING IN, LET'S FIX SOME SOUP AND SANDWICHES, OK?

YOU KNOW WHAT *YOU* ARE? A DISGRACE, THAT'S WHAT.

THIS BOOK SAYS TIGERS ARE SOLITARY AND SECRETIVE CREATURES.

TRUE. VERY TRUE.

SECRETIVE?

OH, SURE! YOU WOULDN'T *BELIEVE* SOME OF THE SECRETS I KNOW.

REALLY?? LIKE WHAT?

I CAN'T TELL YOU. THEY'RE SECRETS.

YOU CAN TELL ME! I WON'T BLAB! HONEST! TELL ME! PLEASE??

BIG SECRETS! *SECRET* SECRETS! BOY, IF YOU ONLY KNEW! MM-MM!

I DON'T BELIEVE YOU EVEN *HAVE* A SECRET.

THAT'S RIGHT. I DON'T.

YES YOU DO! TELL ME IT! PLEEEZE?

NO!

WHY NOT? WHY CAN'T YOU TELL ME??

IT'S ABOUT *YOU*.

AAAHHH! WHAT IS IT?? TELL ME! TELL ME!

I'VE SAID TOO MUCH ALREADY.

IF YOU WON'T TELL ME YOUR SECRET, I WON'T BE YOUR FRIEND ANY MORE.

I'LL GIVE YOU A HINT, HOW'S THAT?

OK! SHOOT.

THE FLEA MARKET.

"THE FLEA MARKET"?!? WHAT KIND OF LOUSY HINT IS *THAT*?

DO YOU KNOW HOW YOUR PARENTS GOT YOU?

I WAS... *WHY*? WHAT ARE YOU SAYING?

NO MORE HINTS.

I DON'T BELIEVE YOUR DUMB OL' SECRET ABOUT MY PARENTS GETTING ME AT A FLEA MARKET.

IT'S TRUE.

IT IS *NOT*, AND IF *ALL* YOUR SECRETS ARE LIES, YOU CAN JUST KEEP THEM TO YOURSELF.

YOU JUST DON'T WANT TO HEAR HOW LITTLE YOU WENT FOR.

OH, HUSH UP. THIS BOOK ALSO SAYS TIGERS WON'T SHARE THEIR TERRITORY WITH OTHER TIGERS.

I CAN SEE HOW OTHER TIGERS WOULD GET ON ONE'S NERVES.

A NICKEL. THAT'S HOW MUCH YOU COST.

THIS BOOK SAYS TIGERS ARE TERRITORIAL AND WON'T SHARE THEIR GROUND WITH OTHER TIGERS.

I GUESS WE'D BETTER DIVIDE UP THE WOODS THEN. THIS WILL BE MY TERRITORY, AND THAT WILL BE YOURS.

THIS ROCK WILL SEPARATE OUR TWO SIDES. AS ANOTHER TIGER, YOU ARE HEREBY BANISHED FROM THIS SIDE OF THE ROCK.

HA HA HA! LOOK WHAT *I-I-I'M* DOINGGG!

YOU CUT THAT OUT!

MY SIDE OF THE WOODS ABOUNDS IN NATURAL SCENIC SPLENDOR.

YOUR SIDE WALLOWS IN DECAY AND FILTH. MY TERRITORY IS INFINITELY SUPERIOR TO YOURS.

YOUR SIDE IS SMALLER.

HEY!

I'M HUNGRY.

WELL, YOU CAN'T CATCH ANYTHING IN MY TERRITORY. THAT'S WHAT THE BOOK SAYS.

WHAT DO TIGERS EAT IN THE WILD ANYWAY?

THEY CATCH BIG GROSS CATERPILLARS LIKE THAT ONE.

EWWW. IT'S GOT LITTLE SPIKES ALL OVER HIM. TIGERS REALLY EAT THESE?

BY THE TRUCK LOAD. THEY'RE GREAT.

LET ME SEE THE BOOK.

WHO ARE YOU GOING TO BELIEVE, SOME SILLY WRITER OR A REAL TIGER?

SO FAR, I HAVEN'T HAD MUCH FUN AS A TIGER.

I THOUGHT WE'D BE ROMPING AROUND THE WOODS LIKE WE ALWAYS DO, BUT IT TURNS OUT TIGERS DON'T SHARE THEIR TERRITORIES WITH OTHER TIGERS!

SO HERE WE ARE, SITTING ON OPPOSITE SIDES OF A BIG ROCK. WHAT A BLAST.

BEING A TIGER JUST ISN'T ALL IT'S CRACKED UP TO BE.

THAT'S NOT THE HALF OF IT. IT SAYS HERE WE'RE AN ENDANGERED SPECIES!

CALVIN and HOBBES

by WATTERSON

THE LATE CRETACEOUS PERIOD...
WHEN DINOSAURS RULED THE EARTH!

..AND CALVIN RULED THE DINOSAURS!

THE TERRIBLE TYRANNOSAURUS SINKS ITS TEETH INTO A TRICERATOPS!

TRIUMPHANT AGAIN, THE UNDISPUTED KING OF DINOSAURS LETS OUT A MIGHTY ROAR!

WITH SAVAGE FEROCITY, THE MONSTER BEGINS ITS FEAST! LIMB-SEVERING, BONE-CRUNCHING AND TENDON-SNAPPING, HE...

CALVIN! THAT'S DISGUSTING!

FOR HEAVEN'S SAKE, SLOW DOWN AND CHEW QUIETLY!

THE TERRIBLE TYRANNOSAURUS RESUMES EATING, MORTIFIED THAT SOMEONE MIGHT SEE HIM.

LIGHTNING FLASHES! THUNDER RUMBLES ACROSS THE SKY!

HORRIBLY, CALVIN HAS BEEN SEWN TOGETHER FROM CORPSES! A POWER SURGE FORCES BLOOD TO HIS BRAIN!

HE'S...HE'S *ALIVE!*

WELL, LOOK WHO'S UP AND ABOUT.

HELLO, SLEEPYHEAD.

...OGGG...

CALVIN WAKES UP STARING INTO THE EYES OF A BIG FROG.

SEEING CALVIN AWAKE, THE FROG SCRAMBLES DOWN AND FORCES OPEN CALVIN'S MOUTH!

CALVIN TRIES TO FIGHT, BUT THE SLIPPERY AMPHIBIAN INSTANTLY SLIDES IN AND IS SWALLOWED! HOW DISGUSTING!

I DON'T FEEL GOOD.

YOU SOUND AWFUL. YOU'VE GOT A FROG IN YOUR THROAT.

CALVIN THE ELEPHANT WANDERS THE AFRICAN PLAIN.

AT FIVE TONS, HE IS THE LARGEST LAND MAMMAL!

HIS DEAFENING CALL SHATTERS THE EARLY-MORNING TRANQUILITY!

UH OH, I'LL BET HOBBES IS WAITING TO SPRING ON ME AS SOON AS I OPEN THE FRONT DOOR!

I KNOW! I'LL SNEAK AROUND BACK AND SURPRISE *HIM*!

HEH HEH! THERE HE IS, ALL READY TO POUNCE! WHAT A SUCKER!

I'M HOME!

I'VE GOT TO START LISTENING TO THOSE QUIET, NAGGING DOUBTS.

AHH! LUNCH, MY FAVORITE MEAL! AND TODAY'S LUNCH IS *EXTRA* SPECIAL!

EVER SINCE THE WEATHER GOT WARM I'VE BEEN SWATTING FLIES AND SAVING THEM IN A JAR.

FINALLY I GOT ENOUGH BUGS TO MASH THEM INTO A GOOEY PASTE WITH A SPOON.

I CALL IT "BUG BUTTER." CARE FOR A TASTE?

TELL ME, CALVIN, DO YOU HAVE ANY FRIENDS AT *ALL*?

OK, YOU'VE ALL READ THE CHAPTER, SO WHO CAN TELL ME WHAT'S IMPORTANT ABOUT THE BATTLE OF LEXINGTON?

ANYONE?

CALVIN, HOW ABOUT YOU?

HARD TO SAY, MA'AM. I THINK MY CEREBELLUM JUST FUSED.

HEY, MOM, CAN WE GO OUT FOR HAMBURGERS TONIGHT?

NOT TONIGHT, DEAR.

AW, MOM! WHY NOT?

BECAUSE I'M ALREADY FIXING SOMETHING FOR DINNER.

YEAH... I KNOW.

WHY DOES THE SUN SET?

IT'S BECAUSE HOT AIR RISES. THE SUN'S HOT IN THE MIDDLE OF THE DAY, SO IT RISES HIGH IN THE SKY.

IN THE EVENING THEN, IT COOLS DOWN AND SETS.

WHY DOES IT GO FROM EAST TO WEST?

SOLAR WIND.

DEAR!

I'M THINKING OF A NUMBER BETWEEN ONE AND SEVEN HUNDRED BILLION. TRY TO GUESS IT.

ELEVEN?

NOPE. GUESS AGAIN.

SIX MILLION AND FOUR.

NOPE. GUESS AGAIN.

WHAT'S THE MATTER, DON'T YOU LIKE GAMES??

DO YOU BELIEVE OUR DESTINIES ARE DETERMINED BY THE STARS?

NAH.

OH, I DO.

REALLY? HOW COME?

LIFE'S A LOT MORE FUN WHEN YOU'RE NOT RESPONSIBLE FOR YOUR ACTIONS.

CALVIN and HOBBES

by WATTERSON

YAWWNN

DESPITE THAT AMAZING DISPLAY OF CUNNING, REFLEX AND PHYSICAL PROWESS, YOUR TAIL STILL HAS A DEATH GRIP ON YOUR BUTT.

COULD YOU STOP THE ROOM, PLEASE? I'D LIKE TO GET OFF.

EIGHT... NINE... TEN! HERE I COME, READY OR NOT!

ALL RIGHT, GIVE 'EM BACK!

CALVIN, I'D LIKE YOU TO PICK UP ALL THE STICKS AND FALLEN BRANCHES IN THE YARD, SO I CAN MOW IT.

WILL YOU PAY ME?

WELL... OK, I'LL PAY YOU A DOLLAR.

A DOLLAR? I WON'T DO IT FOR LESS THAN TWENTY-FIVE!!

IN A MINUTE YOU'LL DO IT FOR NOTHING, JUST BECAUSE I TOLD YOU TO.

...I'LL TAKE THE DOLLAR.

SMART KID.

OK, OUT OF THE HAMMOCK.

WHAT DO YOU MEAN? THIS ISN'T *YOUR* HAMMOCK.

IT'S MY TURN.

I WAS HERE FIRST. IT'S YOUR TURN WHEN I'M DONE.

IF YOU WON'T GET OUT, THEN I'M COMING IN WITH YOU.

LIKE HECK YOU ARE!

THIS CRUMMY HAMMOCK ALWAYS SAGS.

BAD NEWS ON YOUR POLLS, DAD. YOU DROPPED ANOTHER FIVE POINTS.

IT SEEMS THAT ALTHOUGH YOUR RECOGNITION FACTOR IS HIGH, THE SCANDALS OF YOUR ADMINISTRATION CONTINUE TO HAUNT YOU.

SCANDALS? WHAT SCANDALS?!

BEDTIMEGATE AND HOME-WORKGATE COME READILY TO MIND.

INSTANCES OF TRUE LEADERSHIP. HISTORY WILL VINDICATE ME.

I WONDER WHAT MY NEW DAD WILL LOOK LIKE.

YOU'LL BE GLAD TO KNOW I'VE ANALYZED YOUR POOR SHOWING IN THE POLLS.

I'LL BET.

SEE, YOUR RECORD IN OFFICE IS MISERABLE AND THE CHARACTER ISSUE IS KILLING YOU. YOUR BASIC APPROVAL RATING AMONG SIX-YEAR-OLDS HARDLY REGISTERS.

IF ANYONE EVER NEEDED A SLICK AD CAMPAIGN, IT'S YOU.

LET ME GUESS WHAT YOU HAVE IN MIND.

"THE *NEW* DAD" I CALL IT.

I THINK THE IMAGE WE NEED TO CREATE FOR YOU IS, "REPENTANT, BUT LEARNING."

YOU KNOW, SHOW SOME HUMILITY, AND PRESENT YOURSELF AS A REGULAR GUY TRYING TO LEARN THE ROPES OF A DIFFICULT JOB.

DIFFICULT DOESN'T BEGIN TO DESCRIBE IT.

I WORKED UP SOME SLOGANS. SEE WHAT YOU THINK.

"DAD—GRADUALLY, HE CATCHES ON."
"VOTE DAD! *THIS* TIME, HE'LL DO BETTER."
"TO FORGIVE IS DIVINE—VOTE DAD IN '88."

I GET THE IDEA, CALVIN.

Panel 1: IF YOU WANT TO STAY DAD, YOU'VE GOT TO POLISH YOUR IMAGE.

Panel 2: MY IMAGE. RIGHT. SEE, NOW EVERYONE THINKS YOU'RE INSENSITIVE TO THE LEGITIMATE NEEDS OF MINORS.

Panel 3: A FEW MAGNANIMOUS GESTURES WHILE IN OFFICE NOW MIGHT BE IN ORDER. IF YOUR MIND'S GONE BLANK, I HAVE SOME SUGGESTIONS.

Panel 4: OH, THE SUSPENSE. FOR EXAMPLE, YOU MIGHT REPEAL MANDATORY SCHOOL ATTENDANCE. THAT ALONE COULD ROCKET YOU TO VICTORY.

Panel 5: MUCH AS I APPRECIATE YOUR OFFER, I DON'T THINK I NEED AN IMAGE CONSULTANT.

Panel 6: I PREFER TO LET THE WISDOM OF MY WORDS AND DEEDS SPEAK FOR THEMSELVES.

Panel 7: IN THAT CASE, YOU'LL HAVE A LOT OF TIME TO WRITE YOUR MEMOIRS. WE'LL SEE. NOW IT'S PAST YOUR BEDTIME.

Panel 8: "DAD BURIED IN LANDSLIDE! JUBILANT THRONGS FILL STREETS! STUNNED FATHER INCONSOLABLE— DEMANDS RECOUNT!" GOOD NIGHT.

Calvin and Hobbes

by WATTERSON

YES, YOU CAN CERTAINLY SEE FAR FROM UP HERE.

I CALL THIS "LOOKOUT" HILL.

I CALL IT "LOOKOUT" HILL BECAUSE THAT'S WHAT YOU YELL WHENEVER WE GO DOWN IT.

YOU KNOW, SOMETIMES IT SEEMS THINGS GO BY TOO QUICKLY.

WE'RE SO BUSY WATCHING OUT FOR WHAT'S JUST AHEAD OF US THAT WE DON'T TAKE THE TIME TO ENJOY WHERE WE ARE.

DAYS GO BY AND WE HARDLY NOTICE THEM. LIFE BECOMES A BLUR.

OFTEN IT TAKES SOME CALAMITY TO MAKE US LIVE IN THE PRESENT.

THEN SUDDENLY WE WAKE UP AND SEE ALL THE MISTAKES WE'VE MADE, BUT IT'S TOO LATE TO CHANGE ANYTHING.

IT'S LIKE... ..IT'S LIKE...

IT'S LIKE WHAT?

IT'S LIKE *SOME*THING... I JUST CAN'T THINK OF IT.

HERE I AM, WAITING FOR THE BUS. ELEVEN MORE YEARS OF SCHOOL TO GO. THEN COLLEGE, THEN MAYBE GRADUATE SCHOOL, AND THEN I WORK UNTIL I DIE.

WHAT KIND OF WORLD *IS* THIS?! YOU ONLY GET FIVE YEARS TO BE A KID??

WHAT ABOUT EXPLORING AND DISCOVERING AND PLAYING? THOSE THINGS ARE IMPORTANT, TOO!

WELL, YOU STILL HAVE AFTERNOONS AND WEEKENDS.

THAT'S WHEN I WATCH TV.

LOOK, HOBBES, I GOT A MODEL AIRPLANE. WANT TO HELP ME BUILD IT?

SURE.

WOW, A PHANTOM JET! I CAN'T WAIT UNTIL IT'S DONE!

LOOK AT ALL THE LITTLE PIECES.

HERE, YOU PUT THOSE PIECES TOGETHER, AND I'LL DO THESE. THEN WE'LL STICK YOURS ON MINE, OK?

SHOULDN'T WE READ THE INSTRUCTIONS?

DO I *LOOK* LIKE A SISSY?

HEY, THESE INSTRUCTIONS ARE IN THREE DIFFERENT LANGUAGES.

UH OH, I GOT GLUE ON MY HANDS.

IT STARTS IN ENGLISH, BUT THEN IT GOES INTO FRENCH AND SPANISH.

THIS STUFF IS WORSE THAN MOZZARELLA CHEESE.

IT'S HARD TO BELIEVE THIS MODEL IS FOR AGES SIX AND UP.

YECCHH. WHAT A MESS.

YOU HAVE TO BE TRI-LINGUAL JUST TO READ THE DIRECTIONS.

I HOPE MOM LIKES THIS NEWSPAPER HERE ON THE FLOOR, BECAUSE IT'S SURE NOT GOING ANYWHERE.

CALVIN and HOBBES

by WATTERSON

A VOICE CACKLES IN CALVIN'S RADIO. "ENEMY FIGHTERS AT TWO O'CLOCK!"

ROGER. WHAT SHOULD I DO UNTIL THEN?

CALVIN'S F-4 PHANTOM SCREAMS ACROSS THE SKY!

BUT WHAT'S THIS? THE CANOPY GLASS IS ALL SMEARED! HE CAN HARDLY SEE THROUGH IT!

OH, NO! THE THROTTLE SNAPS OFF IN HIS HAND!

CALVIN'S ONLY HOPE IS TO LAND, BUT THE WHEELS REFUSE TO OPEN! THEY'RE STUCK!

FRANTICALLY CALVIN TRIES TO EJECT, BUT THE COCKPIT IS FUSED TOGETHER! HIS JET IS A HOPELESS MESS! EVERYTHING IS GOING WRONG!

STUPID MODEL.

HEY, SUSIE, GUESS WHAT I HAVE IN MY HANDS!

IS IT DISGUSTING?

UM... ..WELL...

IS IT SOME CREEPY, GOOEY THING THAT NO ONE IN HIS RIGHT MIND WOULD EVER, EVER WANT TO LOOK AT?

UH... I.. SUPPOSE THAT DEPENDS ON YOUR POINT OF VIEW...

FORGET IT. I'M NOT GUESSING.

YOU MIGHT AS WELL. YOU'RE NINE-TENTHS THERE.

MOM, WAS I EVER A GRUB?

A WHAT?

YOU KNOW, A LARVA. DID I REALLY PUPATE AT AGE TWO?

DON'T BE DISGUSTING! OF COURSE NOT! WHERE DID YOU EVER GET THAT AWFUL IDEA?!

YOU SHOULD GET YOUR STORIES STRAIGHT WITH MOM, MR. BRITANNICA!

HOW CAN YOU STAND THESE CARTOONS?

THEY'RE JUST HALF-HOUR COMMERCIALS FOR TOYS. AND WHEN THEY'RE NOT BORING, THEY'RE PREACHY.

AND THESE CHARACTERS DON'T EVEN *MOVE*. THEY JUST STAND AROUND BLINKING! WHAT KIND OF CARTOON IS *THAT*?

MEET MY DAD, THE GENE SISKEL OF SATURDAY MORNING TV.

CALVIN and HOBBES
by WATTERSON

C'MON, HOBBES. LET ME UP INTO THE TREE FORT.

SAY THE PASSWORD.

NO! YOU KNOW IT'S ME! LET ME UP!

YOU MAY BE SOME OTHER KID IN DISGUISE.

IT'S *ME*, CALVIN! LET ME UP, YOU HAIRBALL BARFER!

AN INSULT! WELL, YOU CAN JUST STAY DOWN THERE *FOREVER*, MR. STINKER.

OH, NO! HERE COMES SUSIE! LET ME UP QUICK, SO WE CAN THROW THINGS AT HER! HURRY! LET DOWN THE ROPE!

LA DE DA DUM DOO ♪ ♫

SHE'S COMING! QUICK! LET DOWN THE ROPE! I'M SORRY I INSULTED YOU! OK? SEE, I SAID I WAS SORRY! CAN'T YOU LET DOWN THE ROPE?!

YOU HAVE TO SAY THE PASSWORD.

..Verse Seven: TIGERS ARE PERFECT, THE E-PIT-O-ME OF GOOD LOOKS AND GRACE AND QUIET..UH..UM..DIGNITY.

I WAS GOING TO ASK YOU TO COME OVER AND PLAY HOUSE, BUT I THINK YOU'D BE A WEIRD EXAMPLE FOR OUR CHILDREN.

ONE OF THESE DAYS I'M GOING TO MAKE YOU INTO A RUG! YOU HEAR ME?? A RUG!

CAN I USE THE GARDEN SHOVEL?

WHAT DO YOU WANT IT FOR?

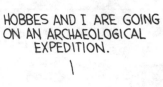

HOBBES AND I ARE GOING ON AN ARCHAEOLOGICAL EXPEDITION.

IF YOU'RE LOOKING FOR FOSSILIZED REMAINS, YOU SHOULD DIG THROUGH YOUR ROOM.

HA HA. SOMEDAY I'LL NAME AN AUSTRALOPITHECUS WOMAN AFTER YOU.

NATTERSON

I'VE BEEN READING UP ON PALEONTOLOGY. IT'S AMAZING STUFF.

SCIENTISTS CAN TELL HOW OLD SOMETHING IS JUST BY ANALYZING THE LAYERS OF DIRT IT'S IN.

HEY!

WHY, YOU MUST BE SIX YEARS OLD.

OH, YOU'RE A SCREAM.

ARCHAEOLOGISTS DIG SLOWLY AND CAREFULLY, USING SMALL, DELICATE TOOLS.

EACH ROCK HAS TO BE PAINSTAKINGLY BRUSHED AND SCRAPED SO NOTHING IS BROKEN OR MISSED.

WATTERSON

DIG DIG SCRAPE SCRAPE BRUSH BRUSH

ARCHAEOLOGISTS HAVE THE MOST MIND-NUMBING JOB ON THE PLANET.

I DON'T THINK YOUR DAD WILL WANT TO SHAVE WITH THIS TOMORROW.

GOSH, LOOK AT ALL THE DINOSAUR BONES WE DISCOVERED.

LET'S GLUE THEM TOGETHER SO WE CAN SEE HOW THEY FIT. THEN YOU CAN DRAW A RECONSTRUCTION OF THE ACTUAL DINOSAUR.

AFTER THAT, WE'LL WRITE UP OUR FINDINGS, AND GET THEM PUBLISHED IN A SCIENTIFIC JOURNAL.

THEN WE'LL WIN THE NOBEL PRIZE, GET RICH, AND GO ON TALK SHOWS.

WHAT ABOUT BABES? WHEN DO WE GET THOSE?

WELL, HERE'S THE COMPLETE SKELETON AS NEAR AS *I* CAN FIGURE OUT.

TRY TO DRAW THE DINOSAUR AS IT REALLY LOOKED WITH MUSCLES AND SKIN.

RIGHT.

WHAT'S IT DOING? WHISTLING?

YOU TELL ME. MAYBE IT'S PUCKERING UP.

SEE THE DINOSAUR SKELETON WE DISCOVERED AND ASSEMBLED?

I'M GOING TO CALL THE NATURAL HISTORY MUSEUM AND TELL THEM THEY CAN HAVE IT FOR TEN BILLION DOLLARS.

THOSE ARE ...UM... PECULIAR BONES.

DO YOU THINK I SHOULD ASK FOR MORE MONEY?

THAT'S NOT *QUITE* WHAT I MEANT.

MOM SAYS SHE DOESN'T THINK WE'VE FOUND A SKELETON AT ALL.

SHE SAYS WE JUST DUG UP SOME TRASH SOMEBODY LITTERED.

OUR DINOSAUR IS A FRAUD.

I GUESS IT WOULDN'T BE RIGHT TO SELL IT TO A MUSEUM THEN.

NOT AT FULL PRICE, ANYWAY.

PSST...SUSIE! CAN I COPY YOUR PAPER?

NO.

CALVIN!

AAUGHH! I SKINNED MY KNEE! OOH! OW!

AAUGHH! OW! OW!

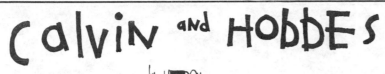

Calvin and HOBBES
by WATTERSON

THE CALL GOES OUT! WE'RE ON THE MOVE!

UP THROUGH THE WINDING MAZE! FASTER! FASTER!

CALVIN SCRAMBLES UP THE GRAINY TUNNEL!

OUT HE POPS INTO THE BLINDING SUN! CALVIN THE ANT RUSHES DOWN THE HILL TO THE BRICK WALK!

OTHER ANTS RUSH AROUND HIM IN THEIR MAD HURRY! CALVIN TRIES TO KEEP UP!

AT LAST HE REACHES THE MONSTROUS DEAD CATERPILLAR! WITHOUT PAUSING, HE HOISTS IT UP!

THE QUEEN DEMANDS HIS TIRELESS TOIL! CALVIN IS BACK OFF TO THE ANT-HILL AS FAST AS HE CAN GO!

WORK, WORK, WORK! THAT'S ALL I'M GOOD FOR AROUND HERE!

I HARDLY THINK PICKING UP YOUR ROOM ONCE IN A WHILE QUALIFIES YOU AS A SLAVE.

Calvin and Hobbes

by WATTERSON

THIS IS CALVIN, YOUR CAPTAIN, SPEAKING...

...JUST TO REASSURE YOU THAT, YES, THERE IS SOMEONE UP FRONT.

CALVIN PILOTS THE JET AIRLINER ACROSS THE COUNTRY AT 35,000 FEET.

HE IS GIVEN CLEARANCE TO LAND. BUT WHAT'S THIS? A PLANE FROM A RIVAL AIRLINE IS MAKING FOR THE SAME RUNWAY TO SHAVE PRECIOUS MINUTES OFF ITS SCHEDULE!

IT'S A 600-MPH GAME OF CHICKEN! CALVIN PULLS BACK ON THE THROTTLE AND LURCHES AHEAD!

THE OTHER PILOT TRIES TO CUT CALVIN OFF WITH A SUDDEN DROP IN ALTITUDE!

CALVIN SWITCHES ON THE "FASTEN SEAT BELT" LIGHT IN THE CABIN, AND DOES A BARREL ROLL!

AT 5 GS, CALVIN HOPES NOT TO BLACK OUT!

AS THEY CLOSE IN ON THE RUNWAY, THE OTHER PILOT HAS NO CHOICE BUT TO PULL UP AND CIRCLE AROUND AGAIN! CALVIN WINS!

HEY, MOM, IS IT TRUE I COULD GET A PILOT'S LICENSE AT AGE 14?

NO.

I HAD NO *IDEA* BINOCULARS WERE SO EXPENSIVE! WE'RE DOOMED! WE'RE DOOMED!

"WE"?

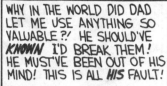

WHY IN THE WORLD DID DAD LET ME USE ANYTHING SO VALUABLE?! HE SHOULD'VE *KNOWN* I'D BREAK THEM! HE MUST'VE BEEN OUT OF HIS MIND! THIS IS ALL *HIS* FAULT!

WHAT AM I GONNA *DO*.?

I SUPPOSE YOU *COULD* JUST TELL HIM WHAT HAPPENED...

...AND MAKE MY GETAWAY WHEN THE CORONARY HITS? SAY, *THAT'S* AN IDEA!

MAYBE WE COULD *GLUE* DAD'S BINOCULARS BACK TOGETHER AND HE WOULDN'T EVEN NOTICE! YOU THINK?

IT DEPENDS. WAS THE CASING JUST CHIPPED A LITTLE, OR DID THE LENS ITSELF GET CRACKED?

WELL, MAYBE YOU'D BETTER LOOK AT IT.

DON'T SNEEZE.

MAYBE YOU SHOULD TELL YOUR *MOM* ABOUT THE BINOCULARS, AND SHE CAN HELP SOMEHOW.

TELL MOM?!? ARE YOU CRAZY?? NO WAY!

WHY NOT? YOU'VE GOT TO TELL *SOMEONE*. MAYBE SHE CAN THINK OF SOMETHING.

AT TIMES LIKE THESE, ALL MOM CAN THINK OF IS HOW LONG SHE WAS IN LABOR WITH ME.

LOOK AT DAD, CALMLY EATING HIS DINNER AS IF NOTHING WAS WRONG.

I KNOW HIM. HIS "DAD RADAR" IS BEEPING LIKE CRAZY. HE KNOWS I BROKE *SOMETHING*, HE JUST DOESN'T KNOW *WHAT*. HE CAN'T NAIL ME UNTIL HE KNOWS FOR SURE. HE'LL JUST WAIT. I KNOW HIM.

HE'S GOING TO JUST SIT THERE EATING AND LET ME STEW IN MY OWN GUILT. HE FIGURES SOONER OR LATER I'LL CRACK.

CALVIN?

AAUGH! I DID IT! I DID IT! I'M SORRY! I DIDN'T MEAN TO!!

..PASS THE UH.. ..THE UH...

YOU *BROKE* THE BINOCULARS?!

DIDN'T I TELL YOU TO BE EXTRA, EXTRA CAREFUL WITH THEM?? ISN'T THAT EXACTLY WHAT I SAID?! WELL?!

THOSE BINOCULARS WERE BRAND NEW! HAVE YOU NO RESPECT FOR OTHER PEOPLE'S PROPERTY.?!?

I HAVE AN IDEA, DAD. LET'S PRETEND I ALREADY FEEL TERRIBLE ABOUT IT, AND THAT YOU DON'T NEED TO RUB IT IN ANY MORE.

I DIDN'T *MEAN* TO BREAK YOUR BINOCULARS, DAD. IT WAS AN ACCIDENT.

(SNIFF) I'M REALLY SORRY. I FELT LIKE I WAS GOING TO BARF ALL AFTERNOON.

WELL, I'M SORRY I YELLED AT YOU LIKE I DID. I SHOULDN'T HAVE BEEN SO ANGRY.

AFTER ALL, IT WAS JUST A PAIR OF BINOCULARS. IN THE BIG SCHEME OF THINGS, THAT'S REALLY NOT SO BAD.

(SNIFF) REALLY?

SURE. ...IN ANOTHER TEN YEARS, YOU'LL PROBABLY BE WRECKING MY *CAR*.

45

RUMBLE RUMBLE

46

Calvin and Hobbes

by Watterson

I GOT A HIT! I GOT A HIT!

ONLY BECAUSE I *LET* YOU!

HA HA! A HOME RUN!

YOU DIDN'T TOUCH ALL THE BASES!

I DID, TOO.

NO, YOU DIDN'T. YOU DIDN'T TOUCH SEVENTH BASE.

YES, I DID! I TOUCHED THE WATER BARREL RIGHT AFTER THE FRONT PORCH.

THAT'S NOT SEVENTH BASE. THAT'S TWELFTH BASE!

I THOUGHT THE GARAGE DOOR WAS TWELFTH.

THE GARAGE DOOR IS TWENTY-THIRD BASE. YOU TOUCHED THEM ALL OUT OF ORDER, AND YOU STILL DIDN'T TOUCH THE SECRET BASE.

THE *SECRET* BASE?? WHAT'S THE SECRET BASE?!

I CAN'T TELL YOU. IT'S A SECRET.

I CAN'T BELIEVE THIS MORONIC SPORT IS OUR NATIONAL PASTIME.

YOU'RE OUT. GIVE ME A DOLLAR.

Calvin and Hobbes by WATTERSON

zzzzzzzzzzzzzz

FILTH! CONTAMINATION! PESTILENCE! HA HA HA!

OF ALL LIVING CREATURES, FEW ARE MORE REPULSIVE THAN CALVIN THE BUG!

HE EXISTS ONLY TO SUCK BLOOD AND TRANSMIT PARASITIC DISEASE!

SEARCHING FOR SOMEONE TO INFECT, CALVIN FLIES LOW OVER THE PICNIC TABLE!

INGREDIENTS: SALT,

HIS SENSITIVE ANTENNAE PICK UP THE SCENT OF HUMAN FLESH!

TOUCHING DOWN, CALVIN INSERTS HIS NEEDLELIKE PROBOSCIS INTO A VEIN! PROTOZOANS IN HIS SALIVA QUICKLY INDUCE PLAGUE!

WILL YOU STOP THAT AWFUL SLURPING?! YOU'RE MAKING ME SICK!

IS THE BEE STILL ON ME OR NOT?

I'M NOT TELLING. YOU CALLED ME A HAIRBALL.

OK, OK, I'M SORRY. YOU'RE NOT A HAIRBALL. NOW, IS THE BEE THERE OR NOT?

NO.

GOOD. NOW I...

I MEANT "NO, THERE *IS* A BEE." TODAY IS OPPOSITE DAY!

DON'T FORGET... AT MIDNIGHT OPPOSITE DAY IS OVER, OK?

"YES."

I'M NOT HAVING DINNER TONIGHT.

OH NO?

NOPE. I'M JUST GOING TO EAT COOKIES IN FRONT OF THE TV.

YOU, YOUNG MAN, ARE GOING TO SIT AT THE TABLE AND EAT WHAT I'VE FIXED, JUST LIKE THE REST OF US.

OH, YEAH. THAT'S WHAT I MEANT.

HELLO, I'M WONDERING IF YOU SELL KEGS OF DYNAMITE.

YOU DON'T? HOW ABOUT PLASTIC EXPLOSIVES?

YOU'RE KIDDING. WELL, WHAT ABOUT LAND MINES? DO YOU SELL THOSE?... YOU DON'T?

LOOK, I'M TRYING TO SEND A GIRL I KNOW INTO DEEP SPACE. PERHAPS YOU COULD SUGGEST SOMETHING.

CALVIN and HOBBES

by WATTERSON

FWOOOOSH

AS IF LIFE ISN'T SHORT ENOUGH.

51

EITHER WE'VE GOT TO GET A CATCHER, OR YOU'VE GOT TO IMPROVE YOUR PITCHING.

GOSH, IT SURE LOOKS LIKE RAIN.

RAIN? WHAT ARE YOU TALKING ABOUT? THERE ISN'T A CLOUD IN THE SKY!

YOU DON'T THINK IT LOOKS LIKE RAIN?

NO. GO AWAY AND STOP BEING SILLY.

 HEY, LOOK! MOM AND DAD ARE THROWING DUFFEL BAGS IN THE CAR. THEY'RE GOING ON VACATION!

AT LAST! FINALLY WE GET THE HOUSE TO OURSELVES! WE CAN STAY UP LATE AND WATCH TV! WE CAN EAT COOKIES FOR DINNER! WE...

 WHAT ARE YOU DOING UP HERE STILL? C'MON, LET'S GO.

ME? GO? GO WHERE?

 ON VACATION! WHAT HAVE WE BEEN PLANNING ALL MONTH?

WITH YOU AND MOM?? WHAT KIND OF VACATION IS *THAT*?!

 SO WHERE ARE WE GOING? I SURE HOPE WE'RE NOT CAMPING AGAIN THIS YEAR.

 WELL, WE ARE.

OH, NO! WHY DO WE HAVE TO GO CAMPING?! I *HATE* CAMPING!

 SWATTING MOSQUITOES WHILE LYING FROZEN AND CRAMPED ON BUMPY ROCKS, WITH NO TV AND ONLY CANNED FOOD TO EAT, IS *NOT* MY IDEA OF A GOOD TIME!

 THAT'S WHY WE BROUGHT BUG SPRAY.

LOOK, JUST LET ME OUT HERE, OK? I'LL HITCH HOME AND SEE YOU WHEN YOU GET BACK, ALL RIGHT?

 REMEMBER LAST YEAR, WHEN IT RAINED ALL WEEK? IT POURED SO HARD WE COULDN'T EVEN MAKE A FIRE.

 WITHOUT QUESTION, THAT WAS ONE OF THE WORST EXPERIENCES OF MY LIFE.

 YES, BUT IT BUILT CHARACTER.

OH SURE.

 WHY CAN'T I EVER BUILD CHARACTER AT A MIAMI CONDO OR A CASINO SOMEWHERE?

WELL, HERE WE ARE! HOME AWAY FROM HOME!

OK, CALVIN, YOU GET OUT WITH YOUR MOM, AND I'LL HAND OUR GEAR TO YOU.

NOW DON'T DROP THIS. IT'S VERY...

OOPS.

PLOONK

DON'T WORRY, DAD. IT'S ONLY ABOUT TEN FEET DEEP. I CAN SEE THE CAMERA AND EVERYTHING.

I AM GOING TO FEED YOU TO THE SEA GULLS, KID.

DEAR, YOU CAME HERE TO RELAX.

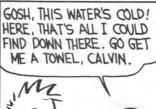

GOSH, THIS WATER'S COLD! HERE, THAT'S ALL I COULD FIND DOWN THERE. GO GET ME A TOWEL, CALVIN.

IT NEVER FAILS. THE ONE BAG THE KID DUMPS IN THE DRINK HAS ALL THE FRAGILE AND PERISHABLE ITEMS IN IT.

WELL, THE WEEK CAN ONLY IMPROVE FROM HERE.

ONE WOULD LIKE TO THINK SO.

HEY, DAD, DID YOU MEAN TO STACK THE TACKLE BOX AND ALL THIS ON YOUR GLASSES?

BOY, DON'T GO NEAR DAD. WHAT A GROUCH!

I DON'T SEE WHY HE CAN'T BE CIVIL JUST BECAUSE I ACCIDENTALLY DROPPED A DUFFEL BAG OVERBOARD AND HE BROKE HIS GLASSES.

ARE YOU GOING TO TELL HIM HE LEFT THE CAR LIGHTS ON BACK WHERE WE GOT THE CANOE?

I THINK YOU SHOULD TELL HIM.

HEY, MOM, DAD AND I ARE GOING FISHING. DON'T YOU WANT TO COME ALONG?

UGGH, NO. THE LAST THING I WANT TO SEE AT THIS UNGODLY HOUR IS A BUNCH OF SLIMY FISH GASPING AND FLOPPING IN THE SLOP AT THE BOTTOM OF A BOAT.

ALL *I'D* LIKE TO SEE IS A DECENT NEWSPAPER, A FRESH MUFFIN AND A POT OF REAL COFFEE.

WHY'D WE EVER COME *HERE* THEN?

GO ASK CONAN THE BARBARIAN.

C'MON, CALVIN. I'LL TEACH YOU TO PUT A WORM ON A HOOK.

AHHH, WHAT A DAY!

UP AT DAWN! FRESH AIR! TRANQUILITY! NO DEMANDS, NO PHONES, NO PRESSURE!

THE WHOLE DAY IS ONE'S OWN! ISN'T THIS GREAT? ISN'T THIS THE LIFE?

SPACEMAN SPIFF, A PRISONER ON THE ZOG SLAVE GALLEY, PLANS HIS DARING OVERBOARD ESCAPE!

AHH, WHAT A DAY!

GOSH, I COULD LOOK AT THE STARS ALL NIGHT.

WITHOUT THE STREETLIGHTS OR POLLUTION HERE, IT SEEMS LIKE YOU CAN SEE FOREVER INTO SPACE.

SNAP   CRUNCH

OF COURSE, IF YOU'VE SEEN ONE STAR, YOU'VE SEEN THEM ALL.

TRUE, TRUE. SHALL WE MOSEY ON BACK TO THE TENT?

LOOK, MOM, THE WATER IS UP TO MY KNEES!

SEE? SEE? LOOK, MOM! THE WATER'S UP TO MY KNEES! SEE? LOOK WHERE THE WATER IS!

NOW LOOK! THE WATER IS *HIGHER* THAN MY KNEES! SEE? LOOK, MOM! SEE?

I'M ENTHRALLED, CALVIN.

YOU'RE NOT EVEN *LOOKING!*

WHATCHA DOIN', DAD? PAINTING A PICTURE?

YEP.

WHAT'S THAT THING? A BRONTOSAURUS WITH RABIES?

IT'S THAT ISLAND OVER THERE.

OH.

HOW FAR CAN YOU SEE WITHOUT YOUR GLASSES? CAN YOU SEE *ME*?

WHEN I LOOK UP, I'D BETTER NOT BE ABLE TO.

HI, MOM!

MM.

DAD'S PAINTING A PICTURE, BUT IT'S NOT COMING OUT SO HOT, AND HE'S IN A REALLY STINKY MOOD. IT'S LIKE, I ASKED HIM ONE LITTLE QUES-TION AND HE NEARLY BIT MY HEAD OFF! I MEAN, IT'S NOT AS IF *I* RUINED HIS LOUSY PICTURE, RIGHT? WHY SHOULD...

CALVIN, CAN'T YOU SEE I'M TRYING TO READ?

EVER NOTICE HOW TENSE GROWN-UPS GET WHEN THEY'RE RECREATING?

THERE'S NOTHING TO *DO* HERE.

THAT'S SORT OF THE POINT, DON'T YOU THINK? IT'S GOOD TO STOP RUNNING AROUND.

SOMETIMES ONE SHOULD JUST LOOK AT THINGS AND THINK ABOUT THINGS, WITHOUT *DOING* THINGS.

YOU'RE CERTAINLY THE EXPERT ON *THAT*.

WHAT I LIKE IS WHEN YOU'RE LOOKING AND THINKING AND LOOKING AND THINKING....AND SUDDENLY YOU WAKE UP.

MOM, CAN HOBBES COME IN SWIMMING WITH ME?

I DON'T THINK HE'D BETTER, CALVIN.

WHY NOT?

UM... TIGERS DON'T SWIM VERY WELL.

THEY DON'T?

FRANKLY, I'M NOT SURE YOUR MOM KNOWS SO MUCH ABOUT TIGERS.

LOOK, WE JUST WANT TO AVOID AN ARGUMENT, RIGHT?

OK, CALVIN, START PACKING UP. WE'RE GOING HOME.

FINALLY!

NOW, NOW. THESE LITTLE OUTINGS ARE VALUABLE EXPERIENCES.

YEAH? HOW?

THEY GIVE US A CHANCE TO BE TOGETHER AS A FAMILY AND LEARN ABOUT OURSELVES.

LIKE HOW WE CAN'T STAND BEING IN SUCH CLOSE PROXIMITY WITH ONE ANOTHER THIS LONG?

EXACTLY.

THIS PROBABLY JUST GOES TO SHOW SOMETHING, BUT I SURE DON'T KNOW WHAT.

THERE'S QUITE A BREEZE UP HERE. I'M REALLY MOVING. THERE'S THE RIVER AND THE TOWN TRIANGLE.

HEY, DOWN THERE! MY NAME IS CALVIN! TELL MY TIGER, HOBBES, I'M BLOWING AWAY ON A BALLOON!

CAN ANYONE HEAR ME? TELL HOBBES HE CAN'T READ MY COMIC BOOKS JUST 'CAUSE I'M NOT AROUND, OK?

...OH, YEAH, TELL MY PARENTS WHAT HAPPENED, TOO, ALL RIGHT? HELLO? HELLO?

UH OH, I'M HEADING INTO A FLOCK OF DUCKS!

EXCUSE ME! COMING THROUGH!

PARDON ME! GANGWAY! BEEP BEEP!

...BOY, IF LOOKS COULD KILL.

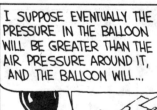

THIS HAS GOT TO BE A DREAM.

WHENEVER YOU FALL FROM TWO MILES UP IN THE SKY, YOU LOOK DOWN, GASP, AND SUDDENLY WAKE UP.

GASP!

GASP
GASP
GASP
GASP
GASP

I WONDER IF MY LIFE WILL FLASH BEFORE MY EYES.

THAT'S THE PROBLEM WITH BEING SIX YEARS OLD...

...MY LIFE WON'T TAKE VERY LONG TO WATCH.

MAYBE I CAN GET A FEW SLOW-MOTION REPLAYS OF THE TIME I SMACKED SUSIE UPSIDE THE HEAD WITH A SLUSHBALL.

SAY, I WONDER IF I HAVE ANY GUM IN MY POCKET. I COULD BLOW A BIG BUBBLE, AND...

NOPE, NO GUM. LET'S TRY *THIS* POCKET.

MY TRANSMOGRIFIER GUN!!

BOY, THESE THINGS COME IN HANDY ALL THE TIME.

 I FORGOT ALL ABOUT MY TRANSMOGRIFIER GUN! NOW I HAVE NOTHING TO WORRY ABOUT!

 I'LL JUST POINT IT AT MYSELF AND TRANSMOGRIFY! I'M SAFE!

 ZAP

 WHERE HAVE YOU BEEN?? I'VE BEEN CALLING AND CALLING. YOUR DINNER'S COLD, I'M SURE.

 I DRIFTED AWAY ON MY BALLOON AND IT POPPED, BUT FORTUNATELY I HAD MY TRANSMOGRIFIER, SO AFTER I MISTAKENLY TURNED MYSELF INTO A SAFE, I TRANSMOGRIFIED INTO A LIGHT PARTICLE AND ZIPPED BACK HOME INSTANTANEOUSLY!

 ...OF COURSE, IF I'D KNOWN WE WERE HAVING *THIS*, I WOULDN'T HAVE HURRIED.

SOMETIME YOU SHOULD TRY TRANSMOGRIFYING YOURSELF INTO SOMEONE WHO OCCASIONALLY MAKES AN OUNCE OF SENSE.

SPACEMAN SPIFF EXPLORES THE OUTERMOST REACHES OF THE UNIVERSE.

BY POPULAR REQUEST.

INTREPID EXPLORER SPACEMAN SPIFF LANDS ON AN UNCHARTED PLANET. WHAT STRANGE WONDERS WILL HE DISCOVER HERE?

SPIFF SETS OUT IN SEARCH OF SENTIENT LIFE!

WHAT A STRANGE PLANET THIS IS! ITS SURFACE IS SURPRISINGLY SOFT AND POROUS!

AND HERE CURIOUS GEYSERS BLAST HOT AIR!

SUDDENLY IT DAWNS ON HIM! SPIFF IS NOT ON THE PLANET'S SURFACE AT ALL! HE'S WALKING ON A RECLINING ALIEN!!

OUR HERO SETS HIS DEATH RAY BLASTER.

ZZ.. MMF HM?

HERE'S HOBBES, BUT WHERE'S CALVIN?

I DON'T SEE HIM.

WHERE COULD HE HAVE GONE? WE JUST TURNED OUR BACKS FOR A MINUTE.

AND WHY DIDN'T HE TAKE HOBBES?

YOU STAY HERE IN CASE HE COMES BACK, AND I'LL GO LOOK FOR HIM.

OK. (SIGH)

BEING A PARENT IS WANTING TO HUG AND STRANGLE YOUR KID AT THE SAME TIME.

SHEESH. CALVIN COULD BE ANYWHERE IN THIS ZOO.

I HOPE HE AT LEAST HAS THE SENSE TO STAY PUT, WHEREVER HE IS.

WHERE WOULD THE LITTLE ROTTER GO IF HE WAS LOST AND SEPARATED FROM HIS STUFFED TOY?

HIS NAME IS HOBBES, AND HE'S... HEY, I'M TALKING TO YOU!!

TIGERS
Panthera tigris

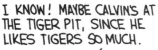

I KNOW! MAYBE CALVIN'S AT THE TIGER PIT, SINCE HE LIKES TIGERS SO MUCH.

HA HA, MAYBE CALVIN'S *IN* THE TIGER PIT, SINCE HE LIKES TIGERS SO MUCH.

YOU FOUND HIM! THANK GOODNESS! WHERE WAS HE?

LOOKING AT THE TIGERS.

I FOLLOWED ANOTHER LADY, THINKING IT WAS MOM, AND THEN WHEN I REALIZED I WAS LOST, I WENT TO ASK THE TIGERS IF THEY'D SEEN HOBBES.

NEXT TIME YOU SHOULD ASK A *PERSON* FOR HELP.

...OH... THAT NEVER OCCURRED TO ME.

ONLY NEXT TIME, THERE WON'T *BE* A NEXT TIME, BECAUSE WE'RE JUST GOING TO TIE YOU TO A STAKE IN THE YARD EVERY WEEKEND.

DEAR!

A FAT LOT OF HELP YOUR COMPATRIOTS WERE, I MIGHT ADD.

DO YOU KNOW WHAT DAY IT IS?

NOPE. WHY?

OH, NO REASON. I WAS JUST CURIOUS.

I SURE LIKE SUMMER VACATION.

SO YOU WANT SOME WATER, HUH? WELL, I'VE GOT A BIG CAN OF IT HERE.

IT'S UP TO *ME* TO DECIDE IF YOU GET WATER OR NOT! *I* CONTROL YOUR FATE! YOUR VERY *LIVES* ARE IN MY HANDS!

WITHOUT *ME* YOU'RE AS GOOD AS DEAD! WITHOUT *ME*, YOU DON'T...

I GOT A HIT!

SAFE!

OK, THAT WAS A SINGLE. I HAVE A GHOST RUNNER HERE NOW, SO I CAN BAT AGAIN.

AND MY GHOST RUNNERS WHO *WERE* ON FIRST AND SECOND BASE ARE NOW ON SECOND AND THIRD, RIGHT?

NOPE. THEY'RE BOTH OUT.

OUT?!

MY GHOST OUTFIELDER TAGGED YOUR GHOST GOING TO THIRD, AND THREW TO MY GHOST SECOND BASEMAN. IT WAS A BRILLIANT DOUBLE PLAY.

THAT NEVER HAPPENED!

YOU'VE GOT TWO OUTS.

WELL, MY GHOST ON FIRST JUST STOLE HOME, SO I'VE GOT ANOTHER RUN! HA HA, SMARTY!

YEAH, WELL, ALL MY OUTFIELD GHOSTS JUST RAN IN AND BEAT THE TOBACCO JUICE OUT OF HIM.

HA! THE GHOST UMPIRE JUST SUSPENDED ALL YOUR GHOSTS FOR ETERNITY. THEY'RE OUT OF THE GAME.

HMPH! IF MY GHOSTS DON'T PLAY, *I* DON'T PLAY.

YOU FORFEIT THE GAME THEN! YOU LOSE AUTOMATICALLY IF YOU QUIT!

THE GHOST CROWD SUPPORTS ME. THEY'RE "BOO"-ING YOU!

SOMETIMES I WISH I LIVED IN A NEIGHBORHOOD WITH MORE KIDS.

CALVIN and HOBBES by WATTERSON

MOM? WHAT, CALVIN?

YOU KNOW THE LIVING ROOM COUCH? WHAT ABOUT IT?

DON'T YOU THINK IT'S TOO WIDE?

I WAS JUST *ASKING!*

WIND WIND

RUMBLE

OH, NO!

POW!

IT WASN'T TUNA! IT WAS PINEAPPLE! *SEE?!*

ALL CANS SOUND THE SAME.

THE PROBLEM WITH HAVING A TIGER FOR A FRIEND IS THAT HE ALWAYS APPEARS OUT OF NOWHERE, COMING RIGHT AT YOU AT A GOOD 90 MILES AN HOUR!

AAH!

WHEW I THOUGHT I HEARD HIM. ...GOSH, MY HEART IS STILL POUNDING. WHERE *IS* HE ??

OH, *THERE'S* HOBBES. THANK GOODNESS.

YOU HAVEN'T BEEN LOOKING WELL, CALVIN. MAYBE YOU SHOULD GO TO BED EARLIER.

Calvin and Hobbes
by WATTERSON

BOY, WHAT A BEAUTIFUL SUMMER MORNING, HUH, DAD? TOO BAD YOU CAN'T STAY HOME TO ENJOY IT.

WHEN YOU'RE OLD, YOU'LL BE SORRY YOU NEVER TOOK ADVANTAGE OF DAYS LIKE THESE, BUT OF COURSE, THAT'S FAR OFF, AND IN THE MEANTIME, THERE'S LOTS OF WORK TO BE DONE.

YEP, YOU'D BETTER GO TO WORK. HAVE A GOOD LONG DRIVE IN TRAFFIC. MAYBE YOU'LL GET HOME IN TIME TO WATCH THE SUN SET... IF YOU CAN STAY AWAKE. SO LONG!

GOLLY, I'D HATE TO HAVE A KID LIKE ME.

WHAT WOULD YOU DO IF I CREAMED YOU WITH THIS WATER BALLOON RIGHT NOW?

TAKE THE WORST THING YOU CAN IMAGINE, AND IMAGINE SOMETHING A HUNDRED TIMES WORSE THAN THAT.

YOU'D DO *THAT*?

NO, I'D DO SOMETHING EVEN WORSE.

HE PIQUED MY CURIOSITY.

BIP

WHEEEE.

77

WHAT ARE YOU DOING WITH ALL YOUR DAD'S TOOLS IN THE BATHROOM?

THIS FAUCET DRIPS, SO I'M GOING TO FIX IT.

YOU'RE GOING TO FIX IT?

THAT'S WHAT I SAID.

..AND YOU CAN KEEP YOUR COMMENTS TO YOURSELF, DR. DOOM.

I DIDN'T SAY ANYTHING.

FIXING A FAUCET IS EASY. ALL YOU DO IS TAKE IT APART, SEE WHAT'S LEAKING, PLUG IT UP, AND PUT IT BACK TOGETHER.

DOES YOUR MOM KNOW YOU'RE DOING THIS?

NOPE. IT'S GOING TO BE A SURPRISE.

AND WE ALL KNOW HOW SHE LOVES SURPRISES.

I CAN'T GET THIS HANDLE OFF. PASS ME THE HACK-SAW, WILL YOU?

AREN'T YOU SUPPOSED TO TURN THE WATER OFF BEFORE YOU TAKE APART A FAUCET?

THAT'S THE PROBLEM I'M TRYING TO FIX, YOU MORON! I CAN'T TURN THE WATER OFF BECAUSE THE FAUCET LEAKS!

SHEESH, WHERE WERE *YOU* WHEN THEY WERE PASSING OUT BRAINS?

OH NO! AUGHH! ACKK!

I'LL GET YOU SOME PAPER AND CARBONS FOR YOUR WRITTEN APOLOGY.

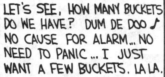

cALVIN and HOBBES by WATTERSON

DINOSAURS EVERYWHERE FLEE FOR THEIR LIVES!

CALVIN IS COMING!

THE LATE CRETACEOUS: THE LAST EPOCH OF THE MIGHTY DINOSAURS!

KING OF THE THUNDER LIZARDS IS THE FEARSOME CALVIN, THE TYRANNOSAURUS!

SEVEN TONS OF MUSCLE AND TEETH, HE SEARCHES FOR PREY!

CALVIN, FOR GOODNESS' SAKE, STOP STOMPING AROUND! YOU'RE DRIVING ME CRAZY!

POW! CHOMP!

HOW DID THE FEARSOME TYRANNOSAURUS BECOME EXTINCT? NOW WE KNOW!

EVERYTHING FLOATS RANDOMLY IN THE ROOM! THERE'S NO GRAVITY!

CALVIN PUSHES OFF THE CEILING AT A SHARP ANGLE, AIMING FOR THE HALLWAY!

HE GLIDES WITH UNCHECKED MOMENTUM, TURNING HIMSELF TO BE ABLE TO PUSH OFF THE NEXT STATIONARY SURFACE.

C'MON, YOU! OUTSIDE! YOU'RE REALLY BOUNCING OFF THE WALLS TODAY.

AW, MOM.

EXTRA PANTS...

THREE SHIRTS, TWO SWEATERS, TWO SWEATSHIRTS...

ANOTHER PAIR OF PANTS...

STILL TRYING TO LEARN TO RIDE THAT BICYCLE, EH?

I DON'T NEED ANY COMMENTS FROM YOU.

A SHADOW FALLS OVER THE LARGE CITY SKYSCRAPERS!

IT'S A GIGANTIC ANT! WITH ONE FOOTSTEP, IT PULVERIZES THE ENTIRE DOWNTOWN! MILLIONS DIE INSTANTLY!

THE ANT BRUSHES THE CITY OFF THE MAP! PEOPLE FLOOD THE STREETS IN PANIC, ONLY TO BE SMASHED IN THE HORRIBLE WRECKAGE!

WELL... MAYBE I WON'T...

TRIP

BAP

WHACK

BAP

I'M HUNGRY.

TOO BAD. BREAKFAST ISN'T UNTIL TOMORROW.

MY TUMMY'S GROWLING.

HUSH.

MOST PEOPLE DON'T SLEEP WELL NEXT TO A HUNGRY TIGER.

SOMETIMES I SURE WISH I HAD A DOG.

MORE TUNA AND LESS MAYONNAISE.

OH, NO! THERE'S A TYRANNOSAURUS IN THE GROCERY STORE!

THE DINOSAUR HEADS FOR THE MEAT DEPARTMENT AND DEVOURS THE BUTCHER!

SHOPPERS EVERYWHERE FLEE FOR THEIR LIVES! IT'S MAYHEM, DESTRUCTION AND CARNAGE IN THE AISLES!

OH, NO! CALVIN, CAN'T I TAKE YOU *ANYWHERE*?!

NOW THE TYRANNOSAURUS WANTS COOKIES!

PLANET CALVIN MOVES ACROSS THE SOLAR SYSTEM.

NOBODY NOTICES UNTIL HIS ORBIT TAKES HIM DIRECTLY BETWEEN THE SUN AND EARTH.

CALVIN CAUSES A TOTAL SOLAR ECLIPSE! EARTH IS SHROUDED IN DARKNESS. HOW LONG WILL CALVIN STAY THERE?!

COULD YOU MOVE, PLEASE? YOU'RE IN MY LIGHT.

HA HA HAAA!

ELECTION DAY IS COMING UP. HAVE YOU DECIDED ON A RUNNING MATE?

A RUNNING MATE?

SURE. YOU CAN'T BE ELECTED DAD WITHOUT A MOM, RIGHT?

ARE YOU GOING TO KEEP THE MOM I'VE HAD, OR GET A NEW RUNNING MATE?

GEE...

BEDTIME, CALVIN.

OF COURSE I'LL STICK WITH YOUR MOM.

AWW...

ALL RIGHT, ALL RIGHT! I'M *GOING!*

HEY! LEGGO! I CAN WALK MYSELF! I JUST HAVE TO... *OK!* LOOK, I'M GOING! I'M GOING!

SURE, YOU THINK SCHOOL'S GREAT *NOW*, BUT IN A COUPLE OF HOURS YOU'LL *MISS* ME! YOU'LL SEE!

THERE GOES CALVIN OFF TO SCHOOL. HE SURE PUT UP A FUSS.

WELL, HE'LL HAVE FUN ONCE HE GETS THERE.

SEE, HE'S EVEN RUNNING NOW. HE'S ALL EXCITED ABOUT...

HEY! CALVIN, THE BUS STOP IS *THAT* WAY! COME BACK HERE!

I CAN'T BELIEVE I'M HERE WAITING TO GO TO SCHOOL. WHAT HAPPENED TO SUMMER?

GOSH, I COULDN'T *WAIT* FOR TODAY! SOON WE'LL BE MAKING NEW FRIENDS, LEARNING ALL SORTS OF IMPORTANT THINGS, AND...

WHAT'S THE MATTER WITH *YOU*??

YOUR BANGS DO A GOOD JOB OF COVERING UP THE LOBOTOMY STITCHES.

Calvin and Hobbes

by WATTERSON

SCHOOL'S OUT! FREE AT LAST!

AND JUST SIX PRECIOUS HOURS BEFORE BED TO FORGET EVERYTHING I LEARNED TODAY.

I HATE COMING HOME FROM SCHOOL. I NEVER KNOW IF HOBBES IS WAITING TO POUNCE ON ME.

MAYBE I CAN STAND OFF TO THE SIDE HERE, AND PUSH THE DOOR OPEN WITH A STICK.

I'M HOME!

WHAT DO YOU DO, WAIT UNTIL YOU SEE THE WHITES OF MY EYES?!?

BOY, YOU SHOULD'VE *SEEN* THEM! THEY WERE AS BIG AS DINNER PLATES! HOO HOO HOO!

93

HAVE YOU BEEN READING THE PAPERS? GROWN-UPS REALLY HAVE THE WORLD FOULED UP.

ACID RAIN, TOXIC WASTES, HOLES IN THE OZONE, SEWAGE IN THE OCEANS, AND ON AND ON!

THE ONLY BRIGHT SIDE TO ALL THIS IS THAT EVENTUALLY THERE MAY NOT BE A PIECE OF THE PLANET WORTH FIGHTING OVER.

YOU'RE PACKING?

YEP. GET YOUR TOOTHBRUSH, HOBBES. WE'RE OUTTA HERE.

IT'S AN OUTRAGE HOW GROWN-UPS HAVE POLLUTED THE EARTH! I REFUSE TO INHERIT A SPOILED PLANET! I'M LEAVING!

REALLY? WHERE TO??

YOU KNOW, SOMETIMES YOU'RE A REAL LOAD TO HAVE AROUND.

I WAS JUST ASKING!

HOW ABOUT MARS? WE COULD GO THERE TO AVOID EARTH'S POLLUTION.

YEAH! IF WE GO NOW, WE CAN CLAIM IT AND KEEP EVERYONE ELSE OFF IT.

OK, IT'S SETTLED. MARS IT IS.

YOU FINISH PACKING. I'LL GO GET THE WAGON.

WE'RE GOING IN THE WAGON?

OF COURSE! WHAT DID YOU WANT TO DO? FLAP YOUR ARMS?

I GUESS I HADN'T THOUGHT ABOUT THAT PART.

OBVIOUSLY.

SPACE TRAVEL MAKES YOU REALIZE JUST HOW SMALL WE REALLY ARE.

WHEN YOU SEE EARTH AS A TINY BLUE SPECK IN THE INFINITE REACHES OF SPACE, YOU HAVE TO WONDER ABOUT THE MYSTERIES OF CREATION.

SURELY WE'RE ALL PART OF SOME GREAT DESIGN, NO MORE OR LESS IMPORTANT THAN ANYTHING ELSE IN THE UNIVERSE. SURELY EVERYTHING FITS TOGETHER AND HAS A PURPOSE, A REASON FOR BEING. DOESN'T IT MAKE YOU WONDER?

I WONDER WHAT HAPPENS IF YOU THROW UP IN ZERO GRAVITY.

MAYBE YOU SHOULD WONDER WHAT IT'S LIKE TO WALK HOME.

HANG ON! WE'RE COMING IN THROUGH MARS' ATMOSPHERE.

BONK
BONK

WE'VE LANDED! WE'RE THE FIRST ONES TO EVER SET FOOT ON ANOTHER PLANET! WHAT A HISTORIC MOMENT!

I STILL CAN'T BELIEVE YOU FORGOT THE CAMERA.

I REMEMBERED IT. *YOU* JUST DIDN'T WANT TO TURN AROUND.

SEE ANY SIGNS OF MARTIAN LIFE?

NOT YET...

HEY, LOOK! IT'S THE OLD "VIKING" SPACECRAFT THAT LANDED HERE IN THE '70s!

GOSH, I WONDER IF IT'S STILL WORKING.

BLAHHHH HOOP HOOP BOOLA ACKACKACK BOOLA

THAT OUGHT TO BLOW SOME CIRCUITS AT NASA!

HEE HEE HEE! I'VE ALWAYS WANTED TO DO SOMETHING LIKE THAT.

WELL, THIS IS OUR NEW HOME. I GUESS WE SHOULD UNPACK AND SET UP CAMP.

COMIC BOOKS... COMIC BOOKS.. TUNA... SOME CANDY BARS... MORE TUNA...TOOTHBRUSHES... A CAN OPENER...LOOKS LIKE WE'RE ALL SET.

WHAT'S THIS?

A NIGHT LIGHT. I THOUGHT IT MIGHT BE SCARY SLEEPING ON A NEW PLANET.

BOY, YOU THOUGHT OF EVERYTHING.

NOW WE HAVE TO FIND AN OUTLET.

YEP, MARS MAY BE A LITTLE DULL, BUT IT'S BETTER THAN EARTH.

CRUNCH CRUNCH

WE'VE GOT A WHOLE PLANET TO OURSELVES. BRAND NEW AND UNSPOILED. NO PEOPLE, NO POLLUTION.

NOTHING BUT RUGGED, NATURAL BEAUTY AS FAR AS THE EYE CAN SEE.

THAT'S NOT YOUR CANDY BAR WRAPPER OVER THERE, IS IT?

IT WAS JUST THERE A MINUTE! *I* WASN'T GOING TO LEAVE IT.

I DON'T KNOW ABOUT YOU, BUT I *LIKE* IT HERE ON MARS.

I DO TOO. IT'S VERY PEACEFUL.

NOT ONLY THAT, BUT WE DON'T HAVE **MOM** HERE TO BOSS US AROUND! NO EARLY BEDTIME, NO BATHS, NO DISGUSTING DINNERS, NO...

DID THAT ROCK JUST MOVE??

MOMMMMM!!

I GUESS WE SHOULD GO HOME TO EARTH.

YEAH, WE MAY NOT BE WELCOME HERE.

WE OUGHT TO FIX UP OUR OWN PLANET BEFORE WE GO MESSING AROUND WITH OTHER PEOPLE'S PLANETS.

AFTER ALL, THERE'S ONLY ONE EARTH, AND IT'S GOT TO LAST US A WHILE.

WE ALSO SHOULD GO HOME BECAUSE WE'RE CLEAN OUT OF TUNA.

I HOPE MOM AND DAD DIDN'T RENT OUT MY ROOM.

THERE'S EARTH! WE'RE ALMOST HOME!

LOOK, YOU CAN SEE THE CONTINENTS.

HMM... IF I REMEMBER MY ATLAS, WE LIVE IN A BIG, PURPLE COUNTRY.

AND OUR HOUSE IS BY THE GIANT LETTER "E" IN THE WORD "STATES."

HI, DAD! GUESS WHAT HOBBES AND I DID! WE WENT TO MARS!

WELL, WELL.

YEP. WE WERE GOING TO LIVE THERE BECAUSE EARTH IS SO POLLUTED, BUT WE DISCOVERED THAT MARS IS INHABITED, SO WE CAME BACK HOME.

YOU DIDN'T LIKE THE MARTIANS?

NO, THEY DIDN'T LIKE US. I THINK THEY WERE AFRAID WE'D JUNK UP MARS THE WAY WE'VE JUNKED UP EARTH.

WHAT'S MY GOOD BRIEFCASE DOING OUT, AND WHY DOES IT SMELL LIKE TUNA FISH?!

AND CAN YOU BELIEVE IT, DAD? WE GO CLEAR TO MARS, AND DUMB OL' HOBBES FORGETS THE CAMERA!

100

Panel 1: HI SUSIE! GUESS WHAT I BROUGHT FOR LUNCH.

Panel 2: NO! GO SIT BY SOMEONE ELSE, OK? YOU ALWAYS SAY YOUR LUNCH IS SOMETHING REVOLTING, AND I DON'T WANT TO HEAR IT!

Panel 3: GEE WHIZ, WHAT'S WRONG WITH YOU? MY LUNCH IS PEANUT BUTTER. WHAT'S SO DISGUSTING ABOUT THAT?!

Panel 4: HMPH. I'M GLAD THAT ONE DAY OUT OF THE YEAR YOU CAN BE CIVIL. IT'S MY *DESSERT* THAT'S GROSS! LOOK, A THERMOS FULL OF PHLEGM!

Panel 5: CALVIN, WILL YOU RUN AND GET MY PURSE, PLEASE? I NEED THE CALCULATOR. SURE.

Panel 6: HERE YOU ARE. THANKS.

Panel 7: AHEM.

Panel 8: I'M **NOT GOING** TO TIP YOU!! HUH! SEE IF I EVER FETCH ANYTHING AGAIN.

Panel 9: ELECTION DAY IS COMING UP, DAD. PEOPLE WANT TO KNOW WHERE YOU STAND ON THE ISSUES.

Panel 10: SUCH AS? LATER BEDTIMES, EXPANDED TV PRIVILEGES, SHORTER SCHOOL WEEKS, AND LESS DISCIPLINE.

Panel 11: I'M AGAINST THEM ALL. I SEE.

Panel 12: HOW'S YOUR IRA? PRETTY WELL FUNDED? GO TO BED.

CALVIN and HOBBES

by WATTERSON

UH-OH.

SOMETHING IS VERY WRONG HERE.

CALVIN HAS MYSTERIOUSLY SHRUNK TO A QUARTER OF AN INCH TALL!

HOW CAN HE MAKE HIS PLIGHT KNOWN TO HIS PARENTS WHEN HE'S SMALLER THAN A PENNY?

CALVIN GETS AN IDEA! HE GRABS THE LEG OF OF A PASSING HOUSEFLY AND FLIES TO HIS DAD'S CAMERA!

ONCE THERE, HE CLIMBS UP AND SETS THE SELF-TIMER.

JUMPING ON THE SHUTTER, CALVIN HAS FIFTEEN SHORT SECONDS TO GET IN FRONT OF THE LENS!

WITH LUCK, CALVIN'S DAD WILL HAVE THE FILM DEVELOPED SOON, AND DISCOVER WHAT HAS HAPPENED!

WHAT HAPPENED?! LOOK AT ALL THESE TERRIBLE PICTURES! I DON'T REMEMBER TAKING THESE. WHO'S THAT LITTLE SPECK IN THE DISTANCE ALL THE TIME? YOU HAVEN'T BEEN FOOLING WITH MY CAMERA, HAVE YOU?

ME? HECK, NO. MAYBE YOU SHOULD GET THE CAMERA FIXED.

MOMMMM

WHAT'S THE MATTER, CALVIN?

I DON'T FEEL GOOD.

WHAT HURTS?

MY STOMACH. I WANT MOM.

ME? WHAT'S WRONG WITH YOU, FOR CRYING OUT LOUD?!?

YOU CAN ASK HIM. NOW LET ME BACK UNDER THE COVERS.

SHEESH, IT'S TWO IN THE MORNING. WHY DO KIDS ALWAYS FEEL SICK AT TWO IN THE MORNING?

CALVIN PROBABLY JUST ATE TOO MUCH DESSERT. IF HE'S GOING TO GET ME UP AT THIS HOUR, HE'D BETTER REALLY BE SICK.

BARRRFF

I DIDN'T MEAN IT!

HONEY, PIPE DOWN. I'M TRYING TO SLEEP.

IT'S BEEN 20 MINUTES SINCE YOU'VE BEEN SICK, SO LET'S TAKE YOUR TEMPERATURE.

IG GOMFA FOME UBHIGGIN.

WHAT'D YOU SAY, HONEY?

IG GOMFA FOME UBHIGGIN.

AACK! WHY DIDN'T YOU SAY SO? GIVE ME THE THERMOMETER! RUN! RUN!

I THINK THE WORST OF THIS IS OVER, SO JUST TRY TO *GET* SOME SLEEP.

I'M GOING BACK TO BED, BUT GIVE ME A CALL IF YOU FEEL SICK AGAIN, OK? NOW GET SOME REST.

MM HMM.

POOR LITTLE KID.

YECCHHH! THERE IS NOTHING WORSE THAN A SICK ROOMMATE! FACE *THAT* WAY!

Z

??

IT'S SCARY BEING SICK... ESPECIALLY AT NIGHT.

WHAT IF SOMETHING IS *REALLY* WRONG WITH ME, AND I HAVE TO GO TO THE HOSPITAL??

WHAT IF THEY STICK ME FULL OF TUBES AND HOSES? WHAT IF THEY HAVE TO OPERATE? WHAT IF THE OPERATION FAILS? WHAT IF THIS IS MY... MY... LAST NIGHT...*ALIVE??*

THEN I CAN LOOK FORWARD TO HAVING THE BED TO MYSELF TOMORROW.

FEW THINGS ARE LESS COMFORTING THAN A TIGER WHO'S UP TOO LATE.

FEELING ANY BETTER THIS MORNING, CALVIN?

NO.

I GUESS I'D BETTER MAKE YOU AN APPOINTMENT WITH THE DOCTOR.

OK.

IT'S SATURDAY, BY THE WAY. YOU WON'T MISS SCHOOL.

I KNOW.

WELL, IT LOOKS LIKE CALVIN JUST CAUGHT THE BUG GOING AROUND. NOTHING SERIOUS.

KEEP AN EYE ON HIM, AND LET ME KNOW IF HE ISN'T FEELING BETTER SOON.

OK. THANK YOU.

SO LONG, CALVIN. YOU WERE A GOOD PATIENT THIS TIME.

MM.

NOTHING LIKE A LITTLE VIRUS TO TAKE THE EDGE OFF A KID.

I'D STILL RATHER LET HIS TEACHER DEAL WITH HIM.

I GET TO STAY HOME FROM SCHOOL TODAY.

I GET TO LIE IN BED, DRINK TEA, AND READ COMIC BOOKS ALL DAY.

I WISH I COULD DO THIS EVERY DAY.

... LIKE SOME PEOPLE I KNOW.

YOUR MOM DOESN'T BRING *ME* TEA IN BED.

I WANT SOME MORE TOAST.

ROOM SERVICE!!

HA! *THAT* SURE GOT YOU UP HERE QUICK!

TOMORROW YOU'RE GOING TO SCHOOL.

I THINK PEOPLE WORRY TOO MUCH ABOUT LITTLE THINGS.

ALL THEY DO IS MAKE THEMSELVES UNHAPPY THAT WAY.

WHY GET AN ULCER OVER THINGS THAT DON'T REALLY MATTER?

LIKE THE BOOK REPORT YOU'RE SUPPOSED TO BE WRITING NOW ON THE BOOK YOU HAVEN'T READ?

EXACTLY. CASE IN POINT.

WHY IN THE WORLD AM I WAITING IN THE POURING RAIN FOR THE SCHOOL BUS TO TAKE ME SOMEWHERE I DON'T EVEN WANT TO GO?

I GO TO SCHOOL, BUT I NEVER LEARN WHAT I WANT TO KNOW.

I HATE SCHOOL.

EACH DAY I COUNT THE HOURS UNTIL SCHOOL'S OVER. THEN I COUNT THE DAYS UNTIL THE WEEKEND. THEN I COUNT THE WEEKS UNTIL THE MONTH IS OVER, AND THEN THE MONTHS UNTIL SUMMER.

I ALWAYS HAVE TO POSTPONE WHAT I *WANT* TO DO FOR WHAT I *HAVE* TO DO!

WELCOME TO THE WORLD.

WOULD YOU SIGN THIS PARENTAL EXCUSE TO GET ME OUT OF THE NEXT 11½ YEARS OF SCHOOL?

THE VALIANT SPACEMAN SPIFF, INTERGALACTIC EXPLORER, COMES IN OVER THE MOUNTAINS OF A STRANGE PLANET!

OUR HERO DESPERATELY HOPES TO FIND A REST AREA WITH WORKING FACILITIES.

SPACEMAN SPIFF LANDS ON THE DISTANT PLANET ZOKK!

CLIMBING DOWN FROM HIS SPACECRAFT, OUR HERO PREPARES TO EXPLORE THE SURFACE!

UNEXPECTEDLY, SPIFF'S FIRST STEP SENDS HIM CAREENING THROUGH THE SKY!

SPIFF QUICKLY REALIZES THAT PLANET ZOKK HAS ONLY A FRACTION OF EARTH'S GRAVITY!

OOF

WITH PRACTICE, OUR HERO SOON FINDS HE CAN BOUND EFFORTLESSLY ACROSS THE LANDSCAPE!

STOP BOUNCING ON THE BED AND GO TO SLEEP!

DUMB BALLOON.

POOF POOF

POOF POOOF

POOFF

HEY, SUSIE, DID YOU HAVE ANY TROUBLE WITH OUR MATH HOMEWORK LAST NIGHT?

NO, WHY?

I THOUGHT A COUPLE OF THESE WERE TRICKY. CAN I CHECK MY ANSWERS WITH YOURS?

OK.

THANKS. WHAT DID YOU GET FOR QUESTION ONE?

SEVEN.

SEVEN? GOOD, THAT'S WHAT I GOT. WHAT DID YOU GET FOR QUESTION TWO?

DROP DEAD, CALVIN.

EVER SIT AND WATCH ANTS?

LOOK AT THIS ONE. HE'S CARRYING A CRUMB THAT'S BIGGER THAN HE IS, AND HE'S *RUNNING*.

AND IF YOU PUT AN OBSTACLE IN FRONT OF HIM, HE'LL SCRAMBLE LIKE CRAZY UNTIL HE GETS ACROSS IT. HE DOESN'T LET ANYTHING STOP HIM.

I JUST CAN'T IDENTIFY WITH THAT KIND OF WORK ETHIC.

Calvin and Hobbes

by WATTERSON

I FEEL A BIG SNEEZE WELLING UP.

...WHICH IS ALWAYS A SURE SIGN THAT I'M NOT CARRYING A HANDKERCHIEF.

AH... AH... AH..

CH·O·O·O·O·O!

MOM, I SNEEZED AND BLEW MY HEAD OFF!

PULL YOUR SHIRT DOWN, CALVIN. YOU'RE NOT FOOLING ANYONE.

MOM WOULD BE A LOT MORE FUN IF SHE WAS A LITTLE MORE GULLIBLE.

113

LOOK! A BUCKEYE!

ISN'T IT PRETTY? LOOK HOW PERFECT IT IS.

I'M GOING TO KEEP THIS ONE.

WHAT WILL YOU DO WITH IT?

TRY TO DENT SUSIE'S SKULL FROM 50 FEET.

WHAT ARE YOU DOING?

DAD TOLD ME TO GO OUTSIDE, SO I'M DIGGING A HOLE TO CHINA.

IF DAD'S GOING TO BE SUCH A GROUCH, I FIGURE I'LL JUST GO LIVE ON THE OTHER SIDE OF THE PLANET.

YOU CAN COME TOO, IF YOU WANT. THERE'S ANOTHER SHOVEL IN THE GARAGE.

YOU DON'T THINK YOUR DAD WILL GET MAD ABOUT US DIGGING UP THE DRIVEWAY?

OH, YOU KNOW DAD. HE'LL GET MAD NO MATTER *WHERE* WE DIG.

LOOK WHAT MOM MADE ME! A SUPER HERO OUTFIT!

DON'T I LOOK COOL? NOW I CAN FIGHT CRIME WITHOUT ANYONE KNOWING MY TRUE IDENTITY!

YEP, I'M ALL SET NOW!

...SO! SEEN ANY CRIMES?

WHY DO YOU CARE THAT NOBODY KNOWS YOUR IDENTITY?

WELL DAD, WE'RE RIGHT DOWN TO THE WIRE, AND THE POLLS SAY YOU WON'T BE DAD HERE MUCH LONGER.

IT SEEMS YOU'RE JUST NOT LIKABLE ENOUGH. THOSE POLLED CONTINUE TO FIND YOU A COLD FISH.

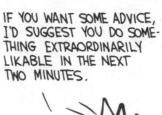

IF YOU WANT SOME ADVICE, I'D SUGGEST YOU DO SOMETHING EXTRAORDINARILY LIKABLE IN THE NEXT TWO MINUTES.

GO TO BED.

NO, NO! IT'S *WAY* TOO LATE TO LEARN HOW TO TELL JOKES.

TEN... FIFTEEN... SIX... TWENTY-TWO...

HIKE!

YAAAA

AUGH!

ANOTHER FIVE YARD LOSS!

WE'VE GOT TO GET SOME OTHER PLAYERS.

BOY, YOU'RE LUCKY *YOU* DON'T HAVE TO GO TO SCHOOL LIKE *I* DO.

YOU DON'T KNOW WHAT IT'S LIKE TO GET UP ON THESE COLD, DARK MORNINGS AND HAVE TO GO SOMEPLACE YOU HATE.

YES I DO.

OH YEAH? HOW COULD YOU?

YOU TELL ME EVERY MORNING.

OH, AM I KEEPING YOU AWAKE?! I'M *SORRY!*

THIS (MMF) ISN'T (OOCH) HOW YOU PLAY THE GAME!

YOU STILL HAVEN'T TACKLED ME!

off the swing, Twinky.

FORGET IT, MOE. I JUST GOT ON. YOU HAVE TO WAIT YOUR TURN LIKE EVERYONE ELSE.

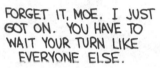

I said, "OFF."

I KEEP FORGETTING THAT RULES ARE ONLY FOR LITTLE NICE PEOPLE.

HIKE!

WHOOPS! HEH HEH..

I'M LOSING THE GAME, BUT WINNING AN AMBULATORY ADULTHOOD.

Calvin and Hobbes

by WATTERSON

RINGGG

WHAT A DAY.

YOU THINK THAT'S FUNNY? COME BACK AND FIGHT, YOU WEASEL!

WHAT HAPPENED TO *YOU*??

DON'T ASK. I'M GOING UPSTAIRS TO CHANGE.

CALVIN'S ROOM · ENTER & DIE

NOT AGAAINN!

WHERE'S CALVIN?

I SENT HIM TO HIS ROOM. I CAUGHT HIM MAKING PRANK CALLS TO PET STORES, ASKING IF THEY'D BUY HIS TIGER.

Calvin: HEY, SUSIE, CAN I BORROW YOUR BLACK CRAYON?

Susie: OK, BUT DON'T BREAK IT, AND DON'T PEEL THE PAPER OFF, AND COLOR WITH ALL SIDES OF IT SO IT STAYS POINTY.

Calvin: GEEZ, WHY DON'T YOU TAKE OUT AN INSURANCE POLICY ON IT?

Susie: JUST DON'T RUIN MY CRAYON. WHAT ARE YOU DRAWING ANYWAY?

Calvin: BLACK BEARS ATTACKING A BLACK FOREST CAMPGROUND AT MIDNIGHT.

Susie: GIVE ME MY CRAYON BACK.

Calvin: HEY! WHAT'S THIS STUFF IN MY SOUP?! YECCHH! IS THIS RICE?!? IT HAD BETTER *NOT* BE!

Mom: RICE? LET ME SEE.

Calvin: LOOK! THESE LITTLE WHITE THINGS! SEE, THERE'S RICE IN MY SOUP! I HATE RICE!

Calvin: I DIDN'T PUT ANY RICE IN. THOSE ARE MAGGOTS.

EWWWW!!

Dad: ANOTHER LOVELY MEAL AT HOME WITH MY FAMILY. ...I WISH MY JOB REQUIRED MORE TRAVEL.

Mom: WELL, HE'S *EATING* IT NOW, RIGHT?

Calvin: GOSH, WAIT 'TIL I TELL EVERYONE AT SCHOOL WHAT *WE* HAD FOR DINNER!

Calvin: UH OH.

HOOP

EEP!

Calvin: I'VE GOT THE HICCUPS SOMETHING TERRIBLE, MOM.

Mom: DRINK SOME WATER.

BANG! I GOTCHA!

ARGG!

GAAACKK

UGHH!

HERE.

WHAT'S THIS?

IT'S YOUR DEATH RATTLE!

SHOOKA SHOOKA

IT MUST BE AWFUL TO BE A GIRL.

I'M SURE IT'S FRUSTRATING KNOWING THAT MEN ARE BIGGER, STRONGER AND BETTER AT ABSTRACT THOUGHT THAN WOMEN.

REALLY, IF YOU'RE A GIRL, WHAT WOULD MAKE YOU GO ON LIVING?

THE THOUGHT OF A JERK LIKE YOU BEGGING ONE OF US FOR A DATE WHEN YOU'RE 17.

HA! NOT ME! GROSS!

THE TYRANNOSAURUS STALKS THE CRETACEOUS SHORES!

THE 5-TON CARNIVOROUS LIZARD CAN RUN FASTER THAN A CHARGING RHINO! WHAT COULD BE MORE HORRIFYING?

STOP THAT CLOMPING AROUND!!

...BESIDES THE BLOOD-CURDLING ROAR OF ITS MOM...

CALVIN and HOBBES

by WATTERSON

I'VE NEVER LIKED CRAYONS VERY MUCH.

THEY JUST DON'T HAVE ANY FLAVOR AT ALL.

FOR AN ART PROJECT, I'M SUPPOSED TO DRAW MY PET, BUT SINCE I DON'T HAVE ONE, I'LL DRAW YOU.

OK!

LOOK FEROCIOUS.

HOW'S THIS?

THAT'S GREAT. HOLD STILL, NOW. HMM... ..MM...

ARRGH! THIS ISN'T COMING OUT GOOD AT ALL! I CAN'T DRAW TIGERS! I HATE THIS CLASS!

HERE, LET ME TRY.

THE GOOD THING ABOUT DRAWING A TIGER IS THAT IT AUTOMATICALLY MAKES YOUR PICTURE FINE ART.

HEY, THAT'S PRETTY GOOD!

PUT SOME HUMAN HEADS AROUND HIM, AS IF HE JUST ATE A VILLAGE.

HOW'S THAT?

BOY, THIS IS GREAT! I'LL HAVE THE BEST PICTURE IN THE WHOLE CLASS! I CAN'T WAIT TO SHOW EVERYONE! WOW! THANKS, HOBBES!

BUT I'M NOT LYING! MY TIGER DREW IT! DO YOU THINK I COULD DRAW SOMETHING THAT GOOD MYSELF??

YES...

PRINCIPAL

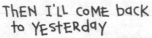

Panel 1: WHEN I GROW UP, I WANT TO BE AN INVENTOR. FIRST I WILL INVENT A TIME MACHINE.

Panel 2: THEN I'LL COME BACK TO YESTERDAY

Panel 3: AND TAKE MYSELF TO TOMORROW

Panel 4: AND SKIP THIS DUMB ASSIGNMENT.

Panel 5: MOMMM, I'M HOME FROM SCHOOL! OPEN THE DOOR FOR ME, OK?

Panel 6: WHAT'S THE MATTER? IT WASN'T LOCKED.

SOMETIMES HOBBES IS WAITING TO POUNCE ON ME AS SOON AS I OPEN THE DOOR.

Panel 7: OH FOR HEAVEN'S SAKE! FROM NOW ON, DON'T CALL ME TO COME TO THE DOOR UNLESS IT'S LOCKED.

HA! I SURE OUT-SMARTED HOBBES *THIS* TIME!

Panel 8: THBBPTT!

SISSY.

Panel 9: BOY, I'M IN A BAD MOOD TODAY! EVERYONE HAD BETTER STEER CLEAR OF ME!

Panel 10: I HATE *EVERYBODY!* AS FAR AS I'M CONCERNED, EVERYONE ON THE PLANET CAN JUST DROP DEAD. PEOPLE ARE SCUM.

Panel 11:

Panel 12: WELL-L-L? DOESN'T ANYONE WANT TO CHEER ME UP?!?

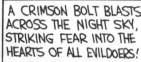

The End